Lesley Anne Ivory's

CATS

BIRTHDAY BOOK

30p

Lesley Anne Ivory's
CATS
BIRTHDAY BOOK

Random Century

First published in Great Britain in 1989 by Ebury Press Stationery
A division of The Random Century Group
20 Vauxhall Bridge Road, London SW1V 2SA
Copyright © Random Century Group 1989
Illustrations copyright © Lesley Anne Ivory 1989
Introduction copyright © Lesley Anne Ivory 1989
Reprinted 1989 (twice), 1990 (twice)

Set in Venture Script by FMT Graphics Limited, Southwark, London
Printed in Hong Kong
Designed by Polly Dawes
ISBN 0 7126 2946 7

Cover illustration: Agneatha.
Back cover illustration: Muppet and
Emu on Amish Log Cabin Patchwork.
Title page illustration: Malteazer in Clover.
Introduction illustration: Gemma on the Jacobean Stool

Introduction

There have always been cats in our family. Granny always had a black cat, and when I was five, kittens were born in the barn next door. One of these, Tissy, was my own first kitten. We grew up together; Tissy was better than a brother or sister because we never quarrelled, and he showed no desire to borrow my paints! His favourite place for a nap was my doll's pram, which was the nearest he came to sharing my toys. He was there all through my school days, but I had grown up and was married before I had the first cat for my little son.

This seemed to set things going, to go on and on having cats. I was unable to resist them. I didn't mean to have them, but I was drawn towards pet shops, and friends' litters, and pet stalls in the market on invisible magnetic wire! When we had kittens of our own by my Gemma, we kept two of these, and found a lovely home for the other two, then one of these had kittens and so on, until the generations built up. Now, counting the ones my sons deliberately 'imported', we have twelve. I need them. First, because I love them and, second, because they are my models.

I had started painting cats from little drawings of Tissy when I was five, and once won a prize at school for a painting of him in a pink doll's high chair. It just fitted him!

Before I specialized in painting cats, I used to paint birds, butterflies, flowers and wildlife subjects, and also did wood engravings of wildlife. It suddenly came to me that it would be a lovely idea to paint a Persian cat on a Persian rug. I did this, and Aries Design published it as a greetings card – and many more followed. At this point I was designing the carpets myself, allowing myself to be heavily influenced by Indian and Persian designs, but my pale ginger tom Spiro *asked* one day to be seen against a William Morris background, and it all seemed so right for me. Now, wherever I go I am obsessed with searching for backgrounds for my cats: from fragmentary relics of Egyptian cloth to pebbles on the beach, or daisies on the lawn.

It has not stopped there. In my 'deepest' paintings I have set my cats amongst actual Egyptian settings. I paired up Julian's 'Twiglet' with the famous Gayer–Anderson cat using a background of pieces of suitable friezes from Sarcophagi, which I thought the cat would feel at home and associated with. Twiglet's wife Gabrielle I have painted on a real Egyptian stool. I felt she had sat there before – 2000 years ago. I don't know how these thoughts for paintings originate; they just come pouring into my head and I cannot paint quickly enough. The cats themselves pose in front of me purposefully. 'What about *this* pose in your next Egyptian, dear?', Twiglet seems to say as he stretches proudly, all four feet on a line.

These two cats in particular seem a natural link from 2000 years ago until now, and the paintings seem to arrange themselves. I cannot begin to describe the number of hours when I must work diligently, often into the night, to achieve each painting. There are no short cuts; I strive for every hair, every blade of grass. Cats are such lovely works of art that no painter can improve on their beautiful forms. My aim is to strive towards as exact a replica as possible and, above all, to catch the nature and aura, which is so individual to each animal. Many people have looked desperately round at my brood and said: 'How on earth do you remember their names, they all look the same to us.' I cannot understand such people; cats are all so different, and having had many of them born in our bedroom, I feel they are my feline children.

Cats are definitely mysterious too, and even mine don't tell me everything! Cats are clean, independent, and a joy to watch, every move a ballet step (pas de chat!). I remember my father visibly relaxing if Tissy should pass by when he was worried about anything. They say people live longer if they live with a cat – what a nice thought for us with twelve of them!

When I stroke our lovely cats, I feel a deep gratitude for their dear little furrinesses for being the essence of my paintings, and my life.

Lesley Anne Ivory

JANUARY

1

2

3

4

5

6

7

THE CHRISTMAS WINDOW.

JANUARY

8

9

10

11

12

13

14

MOTLEY ON AMISH HEXAGONS.

JANUARY

15

16

17

18

19

20

21

RUSKIN ON THE STAIRS.

22

23

24

25

26

27

28

SPIRO ON TUMBLING BLOCKS.

JAN-FEBRUARY

29

30

31

1

2

3

4

BLOSSOM ON PEACOCK FEATHER SCALLOPS.

∽ FEBRUARY ∽

5

6

7

8

9

10

11

GEMMA ON DHURRIE RUG.

~ FEBRUARY ~

12

13

14

15

16

17

18

AGNEATHA AND THE PERSIAN CATS.

FEBRUARY

19

20

21

22

23

24

25

GABBY ON RED GEOMETRIC BACKGROUND.

FEBRUARY-MARCH

26

27

28

29

1

2

3

OCTOPUSSY ON AMISH LOG CABIN QUILT.

MARCH

4

5

6

7

8

9

10

OLLIE ON EASTERN CARPET.

MARCH

11

12

13

14

15

16

17

SPIRO ON PATCHWORK SQUARES.

MARCH

18

19

20

21

22

23

24

PHUAN ON A CHINESE CARPET.

25

26

27

28

29

30

31

D2 ON PERUVIAN WOVEN RUG.

APRIL

1

2

3

4

5

6

7

OCTOPUSSY AND MOTLEY AND BIZZY LIZZIES.

APRIL

8

9

10

11

12

13

14

MOTLEY IN WILD DAFFODILS.

∼ APRIL ∼

15

16

17

18

19

20

21

AGNEATHA ON ROSE HEXAGONS.

22

23

24

25

26

27

28

AGNEATHA IN COWSLIPS.

APRIL-MAY

29

30

1

2

3

4

5

SPIRO ON PATCHWORK TRIANGLES.

MAY

6

7

8

9

10

11

12

CHESTERTON ON A DHURRIE RUG.

MAY

13

14

15

16

17

18

19

OCTOPUSSY IN SPRING FLOWERS.

MAY

20

21

22

23

24

25

26

TWIGLET WITH EGYPTIAN CATS.

MAY-JUNE

27

28

29

30

31

1

2

MALTEAZER WITH WELSH GERANIUM.

JUNE

3

4

5

6

7

8

9

PORTRAIT OF SPIRO.

JUNE

10

11

12

13

14

15

16

TABBY AMONGST PRIMULAS.

JUNE

17

18

19

20

21

22

23

RUSKIN ON FLORAL CARPET.

JUNE

24

25

26

27

28

29

30

SPIRO AND WILLIAM MORRIS.

∾JULY∾

1

2

3

4

5

6

7

BLOSSOM IN DANDELIONS.

～JULY～

8

9

10

11

12

13

14

MUPPET ON ROSE HEXAGONS.

JULY

15

16

17

18

19

20

21

GABRIELLE IN THE DAISIES.

JULY

— 22 —

— 23 —

— 24 —

— 25 —

— 26 —

— 27 —

— 28 —

AGNEATHA ON THE STAIRS.

JULY-AUGUST

29

30

31

1

2

3

4

AGNEATHA AMONGST CHAMOMILE FLOWERS.

AUGUST

5

6

7

8

9

10

11

RUSKIN ON MRS JONES'S CATHEDRAL PATCHWORK.

———————— 12 ————————

———————— 13 ————————

———————— 14 ————————

———————— 15 ————————

———————— 16 ————————

———————— 17 ————————

———————— 18 ————————

PORTRAIT OF OCTOPUSSY.

AUGUST

19

20

21

22

23

24

25

AGNEATHA AND HER FIRST KITTENS ON BLUE PATCHWORK.

26

27

28

29

30

31

1

FIVER ON ORIENTAL RUG.

SEPTEMBER

2

3

4

5

6

7

8

BECKY ON MY FATHER'S CHAIR.

SEPTEMBER

9

10

11

12

13

14

15

MUPPET ON RED CARPET.

SEPTEMBER

16

17

18

19

20

21

22

SPIRO'S CHRISTMAS STOCKING.

SEPTEMBER

23

24

25

26

27

28

29

AGNEATHA ON BLUE FLORAL RUG.

30

1

2

3

4

5

6

OCTOPUSSY IN AUTUMN LEAVES.

OCTOBER

7

8

9

10

11

12

13

FLUFF ON ROMAN PAVEMENT.

OCTOBER

14

15

16

17

18

19

20

GABRIELLE ON EGYPTIAN CHAIR.

OCTOBER

———————— 21 ————————

———————— 22 ————————

———————— 23 ————————

———————— 24 ————————

———————— 25 ————————

———————— 26 ————————

———————— 27 ————————

BECKY ON HEXAGONS.

28

29

30

31

1

2

3

LUCY-LOCKET ON WHEELBACK CHAIR.

NOVEMBER

4

5

6

7

8

9

10

MUPPET NURSING HER KITTENS.

～ NOVEMBER ～

11

12

13

14

15

16

17

RUSKIN ON AN AMISH QUILT.

NOVEMBER

—————— 18 ——————

—————— 19 ——————

—————— 20 ——————

—————— 21 ——————

—————— 22 ——————

—————— 23 ——————

—————— 24 ——————

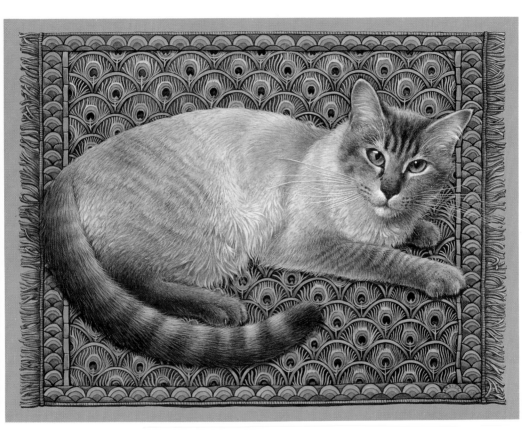

MAUMAU ON A CARPET OF PEACOCK FEATHERS.

NOVEMBER-DECEMBER

25

26

27

28

29

30

1

OCTOPUSSY UNDER THE STAR.

DECEMBER

_____ 2 _____

_____ 3 _____

_____ 4 _____

_____ 5 _____

_____ 6 _____

_____ 7 _____

_____ 8 _____

AGNEATHA UNDER THE HOLLY.

～ DECEMBER ～

——————— 9 ———————

——————— 10 ———————

——————— 11 ———————

——————— 12 ———————

——————— 13 ———————

——————— 14 ———————

——————— 15 ———————

MAUMAU AND THE BLUE GREETINGS CARD.

DECEMBER

16

17

18

19

20

21

22

GEMMA AND THE PINK SUGAR MOUSE.

DECEMBER

23

24

25

26

27

28

29

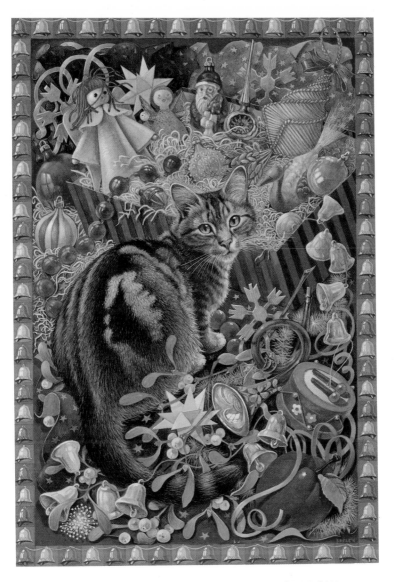

OCTOPUSSY AND THE CHRISTMAS DECORATIONS.

DECEMBER

— *30* —

— *31* —

MOTLEY AND THE CHRISTMAS PUDDINGS.